INFLUEN

Dedicated to Judith Ward, a true influencer

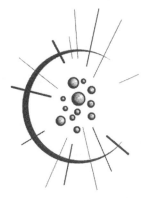

influencers

turning your school
upside down from
the inside out

Chris Evans and Matt Summerfield

A handbook for Urban Saints

survivor

URBAN
SAINTS

Unless otherwise indicated, biblical quotations are from
the New International Version © 1973, 1978, 1984
by the International Bible Society.

Cover design by Mark Prentice

ISBN 978 1 84291 376 5

Survivor is an imprint of
KINGSWAY COMMUNICATIONS LTD
Lottbridge Drove, Eastbourne BN23 6NT, UK.
info@survivor.co.uk

Printed in the USA

influencers

Contents

Background

Chris Evans is Co-ordinator of the St Albans and Harpenden Christian Education Project (STEP). STEP is a collaborative local church initiative designed to see Christianity relevantly and positively represented in secondary schools. Its activities break down the spiritual/secular divide and model and encourage a relevant and active Christianity which is as much needed in the classroom and the corridor, as in the church. STEP seeks to present this Christianity to all pupils, challenging them to live life the way the creator intended.

For more information go to **www.stepschoolswork.org.uk**

Matt Summerfield is Executive Director of Urban Saints. Since 1906 Urban Saints (formerly known as Crusaders) has been reaching out to children and young people with the good news of Jesus Christ. It is passionate about working with children and young people who have no church connection, helping them realise their full God-given potential as they journey from childhood to adulthood. Young people connect with the movement in a variety of ways, including weekly youth groups, special events, holidays, community projects and training programmes. These activities are led by thousands of volunteers who are comprehensively trained and supported in order to help them work effectively and achieve the highest possible standards of youth work practice. While much of Urban Saints' work is in the UK and Ireland, increasingly it is helping indigenous churches within countries in the developing world to set up and run outreach work among unchurched children and young people.

For more specific information go to **www.urbansaints.org**

Introduction

Congratulations! You are taking your next step in a journey that draws you closer to finding out who you are and what you are living for. This book will help you to be better prepared to be a Christian in your community. By your community we mean the places where you hang out, especially your school or college. This book will prepare you for the challenges ahead of you in this life. As you read this book take your time and enjoy both learning and doing.

Throughout history God has always moved through influencers. Influencers are people who bring radical change from within. They're in the world but not of this world. They're people of God's kingdom bringing His good news to everyone. The Bible is full of influencers who changed history. Daniel and Esther were young and exciting people. But what makes them different – what makes them such an exciting part of God's story – is that they were willing to be used. In today's world God is looking for influencers – young people who are willing to be used by God in the places they find themselves. Are you willing to follow in Daniel and Esther's footsteps and believe that you were 'born for such a time as this'?

Influencers is designed to be both fun and challenging. We hope this book will not only make you a better witness but it will encourage and challenge some of your views. Exploring the ideas in this book will prepare you to be God's influencer in your community. This book doesn't have all the answers and may even leave you with new questions. Don't be scared of the questions. Embrace them and chew them over. We are convinced that questions are good; questions suggest that God is bigger than our understanding. Questions help us maintain a sense of perspective and wonder. Treasure the questions!

As you read this book you will realise that there are several things you need to do to complete each chapter. Each chapter is divided into sections. Each section includes tasks you need to perform, things you need to think about and lots of stuff to chat about with a mentor. 'What's a mentor?' you may ask. In order to get the most of *Influencers* you need to have someone older than you in your church who can help you as you work through this resource. We've included some information on selecting a mentor in the next section. We were never supposed to be influencers by ourselves, so make sure you get someone to walk with you on your faith journey.

Remember, being an influencer isn't about passing or failing. It is about growing and influencing. Give everything a go!

We hope you enjoy this opportunity!

Chris Evans and Matt Summerfield

How to Find a Mentor

As we have mentioned, mentors play a vital part in this book. Their job is to help you think about and apply what you are reading. They will also pray for you and help you become responsible for your own spiritual growth.

Choosing a mentor is a difficult process. Not many people mentor teenagers. This is because the idea has never occurred to them. Maybe it hasn't occurred to them because they weren't mentored. Why not break the cycle and give them a chance to change this?

Before you start the *Influencers* programme you need to find someone who is both willing and appropriate to mentor you. A mentor needs to be someone you respect and who is actively seeking God themselves. This doesn't mean they are perfect. It means they are trying hard to follow Jesus for themselves. Your mentor needs to be easily contactable and have time for you. Mentors need to be interested in your spiritual growth and willing to put time into praying for you. We suggest that as you begin to choose your mentor you avoid if possible the following:

- A mentor of the opposite sex
- A mentor who is the same age as you
- A mentor in your family

Think of someone you know who fits the above description. Why not go and talk to your youth leader or church leader and ask them if this prospective mentor would be good? If they say 'yes', go and talk to your prospective mentor, showing them the mentoring guidelines we've included with *Influencers*. The guidelines will help you both decide whether they would make a good mentor. If they would, then you are up and running. If not, then you need to begin thinking about other options. Your youth leader or church leader may have some helpful suggestions.

Once you have a mentor arrange to meet with them regularly

– ideally once a week but certainly no less than once a fort-
night. You can either work through the material with your mentor when you meet together, or alternatively you can work
through it by yourself and discuss what you've worked through
when you meet with your mentor.

Guidelines for Mentoring

If you are reading this then a young person has asked you to consider mentoring them through this course. Perhaps you're wondering if you are qualified for such a task. In our opinion the key criteria for mentoring a young person are:

- If you have been round the Christian block a few times
- If you are trying to be constant in your pursuit of God
- If you have no illusions about your own ability to be holy
- If you are willing to pray
- If you are willing to listen
- If you can exercise both compassion and criticism
- If you genuinely care for the young person

This section helps outline what we understand by the mentoring process. These are not exhaustive guidelines and it's very important that you bring your individual style to the process. We do ask that you read the following and apply it as part of what you do in the spiritual development of your student.

Aim: The mentors are to walk alongside the students in their growth and struggles, providing godly discipleship and accountability.

Minimum time: Twice a month (once to include food if possible!).

Tasks to perform:

- Build a relationship of trust, openness and acceptance where God is at the centre.
- Work with the student through issues of holiness and becoming responsible for their own spiritual growth.
- Chat about relationships with friends, enemies, leaders, and others of significance.
- Discuss learnings from this *Influencers* resource, plus any other things that you have learned from church and personal study.

11

- Advise and pray through issues (both good and bad) in their lives.
- Pray with, and for, the student.
- Model a dependence on God by bringing the issues that come up to Him in prayer.

The following suggestions might also be helpful:

1. Set up an agreed basis for the mentoring relationship, e.g. a contract, saying how differences of opinion, methods of confrontation, ways to encourage, etc. should be dealt with.
2. Book dates in the diary. You could agree that whoever cancels will book the next appointment at the same time.
3. Develop a two-way conversation that does not involve closed questions.
4. Have a checklist of questions that could be covered, but only use if needed. The time should be natural not list-dictated.
5. Sometimes mentors' best intentions can manifest themselves as control. Your job is to facilitate the young person's journey, helping them to think through the issues and leaving them room to make their own choices. Asking questions rather than giving answers is a good principle to avoid controlling the young person.

Over and above working through the material, there may be other questions that you might want to ask from time to time to aid their discipleship. These might include:

- What have you learned since last time?
- What do you sense that God has been doing since we last met?
- What are you finding tough?
- What is God teaching you?
- How are you dealing with your sin?
- Is there anything else I haven't asked you that you want to talk about?

Remember, God has a plan for the young person. God's plan for them extends beyond anything you are aware of. Please begin to dream godly dreams for them. Mentoring times are perfect opportunities to impart these dreams and help them to plan the next steps. Please don't neglect to dream these dreams, since they will be looking to you for help in the future, and through the nature of the relationship will hope that you will be dreaming and praying for them.

If you feel that you need some additional training in mentoring then Urban Saints has produced a video-based training programme which will give you a much deeper grounding in becoming an effective mentor.

INFOCUS VIDEO

At the heart of the video is a desire to see the rediscovery of a holistic, biblical approach to developing young people; an approach we believe is most effective when used within a mentoring context.

- The video is divided into four 15-minute sections, featuring interviews with youth leaders, expert opinion, discussion questions and practical advice.
- An A4 worksheet has been produced for each of the four sections, designed to help teams to work through and reflect on the issues raised.
- We recommend that youth leadership teams work together through all four parts of the video – it will take about two hours including discussion time.

To purchase the mentoring video please contact the Urban Saints Support Centre, Kestin House, 45 Crescent Road, Luton LU2 0AH. Tel: 01582 589850.

Connecting with Other Influencers

Can you imagine what God could do if thousands of young people all across the country were equipped to be influencers in their community – bringing the good news of Jesus Christ to every boy and girl? Do you want to be a part of such a movement? If so, we'd love to hear from you. Our aim is to keep in touch with you as you seek to follow Jesus, encouraging you in the highs and the lows. We'll also keep you posted with radical opportunities to serve out of your comfort zone (see some of the examples below).

So don't delay . . . Register today at **www.urbansaints.org/ insiders** and become part of the *Influencers* movement.

Catalytic Opportunities for Growth

Like you, we long to see a generation of young people make a God-honouring difference in their world, developing their gifts and applying their faith to every situation. *Influencers* will significantly equip you for that task, but sometimes we can all benefit from even greater challenges that will take us way out of our comfort zone, forcing us to depend on God.

To this end, Urban Saints has developed some specific programmes that will support what you do locally with *Influencers*. These programmes aim to catalyse new levels of growth in your relationship with God, and include:

- **Re:Act:** giving young people (14+) practical training and experience in evangelism through large-scale family 'fun days' run across a number of towns in a region of the UK.
- **CRUSOE:** short-term overseas projects in which teams of young people (14+) travel within Europe or worldwide in order to share their faith and serve communities in practical ways.

- **Infusion:** a year-long course that trains teenagers in leadership skills while they help in their local youth or children's group, supervised by one of the experienced leaders.
- **Radish:** a 'year-in' programme of residential weekends, home study and action opportunities to train young people aged 16+ to be radical disciples in their own communities and help them 'unlock' the skills God has given them.
- **STEP-OUT:** a discipleship and mission year out working with Chris's team in the schools in St Albans and Harpenden, bringing the gospel into the classroom, and building relationships with the lost.

See **www.urbansaints.org/insiders** for more details.

Or contact us at Urban Saints Support Centre, Kestin House, 45 Crescent Road, Luton LU2 0AH. Tel: 01582 589850.

Your Key Learning Points

The following is intended as a helpful quick reference for your key learning points from each session. When you've completed a session of *Influencers* turn to this page and summarise what you've learned in a few sentences. If you find that you have only a few minutes to spare then this should provide a useful summary of all that you have learned while progressing through the course.

Key reflections on Session 1 – Catch the Vision

Key reflections on Session 2 – Jesus in the Corridors

Key reflections on Session 3 – Spirit Empowered

Key reflections on Session 4 – Knowing the Father

Key reflections on Session 5 – Kingdom Living

○ —————————————————————————————————

○ —————————————————————————————————

Key reflections on Session 6 – The Ideal Influencer

○ —————————————————————————————————

○ —————————————————————————————————

Key reflections on Session 7 – Counting the Cost

○ —————————————————————————————————

○ —————————————————————————————————

Key reflections on Session 8 – The Influencer

○ —————————————————————————————————

○ —————————————————————————————————

Key reflections on Session 9 – The Shepherd

○ —————————————————————————————————

○ —————————————————————————————————

Key reflections on Session 10 – Learning through God's Discipline

○ —————————————————————————————————

○ —————————————————————————————————

Key reflections on Session 11 – Learning through Self-Discipline

○ —————————————————————————————————

○ —————————————————————————————————

Key reflections on Session 12 – Spread the Word

○ _____

○ _____

Key reflections on Session 13 – Shout It Out!

○ _____

○ _____

Key reflections on Session 14 – Helping People on Their Journey

○ _____

○ _____

Key reflections on Session 15 – How 2

○ _____

○ _____

Key reflections on Session 16 – Putting It All Together

○ _____

○ _____

influencers Your Key Learning Points

Session 1
Catch the Vision

Session aim:

The aim of this session is to help you see the need for God to be at work in your community, through you. God has a vision that every generation will know Him, experiencing His very best life both now and for all eternity. He has called you to get involved in seeing that vision become a reality.

Get motivated!

Have you ever imagined what would happen if Jesus walked the corridors of your school or college today? If the Holy Spirit moved through the vents? If God was respected as the one and only King of the playground?

Well, Jesus might not be physically walking the corridors of your school or college today, but guess what? *You're* there! And He wants to walk the corridors through you, impacting the lives of everyone you meet. Not only that, but you have the Holy Spirit in you and if God is King of your life then there's fantastic news . . .

Be honest! How does it feel to think that God wants to use you to make a difference in your community?

O ———————————————————————

O ———————————————————————

. . . God's kingdom can be built in your community through God at work in you!

It's highly likely that you have mixed feelings about this challenge. Perhaps you're feeling excited about the idea that the creator of the universe wants to work through you, or maybe you're feeling quite scared, wondering what people will think.

For this reason, it's so important that we first catch God's perspective on the need, understanding His vision for the world and His clear call for us to get involved.

If only we could get God's perspective on our situation. Imagine Jesus walking to school or college, turning the corner and seeing the playground full of young people. What would He say?

O————————————————————————

Read Matthew 9:36–38 and sum up what you think Jesus was feeling when He looked at the people as they walked by.

O————————————————————————

O————————————————————————

The image of sheep and shepherds is probably an alien one to us. Imagine Jesus using a more relevant phrase today, e.g. a class without a teacher, an army without a general, or a team without a captain. The point was that the people were lost – they weren't experiencing *real life*. Deep down all people are wondering about their purpose and value, and they will only find the answer to these questions when they come to know their creator personally.

In what ways do you see your friends struggling with life today? Where do they need hope and real life?

O——————————————————————

O——————————————————————

The apostle John was one of Jesus' closest disciples. He spent nearly three years watching what Jesus did. In John's latter years he wrote one of the Gospels and three letters.

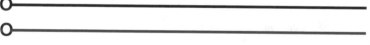

Have a look at the following passages and see if you can summarise the key message that John is trying to communicate about the mission and vision of Jesus: John 3:36, John 5:24, John 6:47, John 10:10 and 1 John 5:11–12.

O——————————————————————

O——————————————————————

God has a vision that '. . . each generation can set its hope anew on God, remembering his glorious miracles and obeying his commands' (Psalm 78:7).

It might be difficult to imagine your non-Christian friends deciding to set their hope on God, in awe of His love and power and obediently following Him. But that really is God's passion and He wants to make that vision a reality through you. Think about it! God wants to involve you in His master plan to see every generation come to know His best life, both now and for all eternity.

If you're still not sure then read these last words of Jesus as recorded in Matthew 28:18–20 and Acts 1:8, which He spoke to His disciples before returning to heaven.

Matthew 28:18–20 tells us:

1. Jesus has all authority over .... and .... (verse 18)

2. He commands us to go and .... (verse 19)

3. We must teach people to .... God (verse 20)

4. Jesus promises to be with us .... (verse 20)

Acts 1:8 tells us:

1. Jesus has given us His ....

2. We will become His ....

So with all this in mind, why not start by thinking about the ways Jesus might want you to get involved in meeting the needs of people in your community? How could you start to be a witness in your community among your friends, teachers, etc.?

Get active!

Through the coming sessions we'll be looking at how you can become the most effective influencer for God. It may all seem a bit scary at the moment, but be assured that God is with you and will help you every step of the way.

As we come to a close in this session, why not take a moment and answer the questions below?

What have you learned about the needs of people who don't know God?

O——————————————————————————

What have you learned about God's vision for every generation?

O——————————————————————————

What have you learned about who God has called to see the vision become a reality?

O——————————————————————————

How are you feeling right now about that challenge?

O——————————————————————————

Take some time to pray honestly before God, asking Him to help you to start to make a difference in your community and see the dream of God realised.

Note: this kind of Christianity comes with a warning. Make sure that your activities respect not only the school, but the individuals involved. Posters telling people they are going to hell can seriously ruin the Christian's voice in school. Run your ideas past your mentor before doing them.

To finish, turn to 'Your Key Learning Points' and write down a few sentences to summarise the key things that you have learned from this session.

Jesus in the Corridors

Session aim:

In the last session we introduced the challenge to catch God's vision for the world and His call for you to get involved. In this session we'll be considering more about what it means to do what Jesus would do if He was physically at your school today.

Get motivated!

It's clear that God is looking for us to be courageous witnesses for Him in our communities. But why is this so important?

Read 2 Corinthians 5:17–20 and match the verses to the statements below.

Christ has made us new people. . .	verse 19
Who have been reconciled to God. . .	verse 17
With our sins no longer counting against us. . .	verse 18
And God wants us to see others reconciled to Him. . .	verse 20
So Christ wants to work through us as His representatives. . .	verse 1

An influencer needs to be like Jesus in their school because. . .

- God has forgiven us and given us a new start – we're His children
- God wants as many people as possible to experience the same new life.

Of course, as we'll discover, being like Christ will mean that there are times you'll have to go against the flow and behave differently. But you have God's permission and help to do this.

Think of all your activities in the week and give examples of various situations you encounter. Then score how much you let Jesus into those situations at present. Be as honest as you can!

Situation

Score [Shade in the circles, 1 being low, 5 being very high]

e.g. Mucking about on the school bus ● ● ● ○ ○

○ ○ ○ ○ ○

○ ○ ○ ○ ○

○ ○ ○ ○ ○

○ ○ ○ ○ ○

○ ○ ○ ○ ○

○ ○ ○ ○ ○

○ ○ ○ ○ ○

continued . . .

influencers 2. Jesus in the Corridors

○ ○ ○ ○ ○

○ ○ ○ ○ ○

Write down your overall observations, having completed this activity:

○——————————————————————————

○——————————————————————————

Think about what you know about Jesus and the things He did when He walked the earth. If you want a great overview of Jesus' life then read the Gospel of Mark – it's only 16 chapters.

Perhaps you're thinking that you could never do the things that Jesus did. You're probably thinking, 'He's so awesome and I'm

List some of the things that Jesus did – we've given an example below. . .

Loved the unlovely

Jesus

What would the reaction be in your school or college if you did the kind of things that Jesus did?

○——————————————————————————

○——————————————————————————

26

just me.' The reality is that we *are* becoming like Jesus. We just need to follow Him and begin to let Him change us so that we behave like Him. In fact, Jesus made an incredible claim about what we could do through Him.

> **Read John 14:12–14 and see what Jesus Himself had to say. What does this passage tell you?**
>
> O ——————————————————————————
>
> O ——————————————————————————

There's one brief word of warning that we need to give here having read this scripture. God always answers every prayer but those answers don't always conform to the solution we prefer. Praying something in Jesus' name is as much about submitting to His will and trusting the result will make God famous.

Get active!

So guess what? Jesus wants us to follow Him and do what He did. But remember He starts where you are. What would be a big step forward for you – something that shows God at work through you? It may be (a) not gossiping, or (b) doing your homework, or (c) praying for a friend.

Write down three practical things that would be good for you to do to be more like Jesus.

1. ....

2. ....

3. ....

Why not pause and pray now that God will help you achieve these things?

To finish, turn to 'Your Key Learning Points' and write down a few sentences to summarise the key things that you have learned from this session.

Session 3
Spirit Empowered

Session aim:
Living as a Christian can be really tough at times but God has not left us without help. In this session we'll discover how the Holy Spirit helps us to follow Christ.

Get motivated!
What kind of food and drink have you consumed in the past week?

Write in the columns below the things you have eaten that you think have been good for you and the stuff that perhaps was not so good.

Healthy

....

....

....

....

Unhealthy

....

....

....

....

What do you think the effect would be if we had a consistently poor diet?

O————————————————————————————

O————————————————————————————

> **Read Ephesians 5:18. Summarise what you think is the key message of this passage.**
>
> O————————————————————————————————
>
> O————————————————————————————————

In the same way that we need to be filled with good food and drink to develop our physical strength, we also need to be filled with God's Holy Spirit in order to have the strength and ability to follow Jesus.

> **What are some of the first words that come into your mind when you hear the words 'Holy Spirit'.**
>
> O————————————————————————————————
>
> O————————————————————————————————

Some people think that the Holy Spirit is like the 'Force' from *Star Wars*. The reality though is that the Holy Spirit is a person. He is part of the Trinity, which we understand as God the Father, Son and Holy Spirit. All are equally God.

God existing in three persons is very tough for us to understand. It might be helpful for you to consider the following illustrations. Consider an egg or a mathematical equation. An egg has three distinct parts, recognised for the individual purposes and properties. The egg is made up of the shell, the yoke and the white. Alternatively consider one times one times one. The result is one! Both show that God is three in one. Considering God as three equal persons in one, however, even with the help

influencers 3. Spirit Empowered

30

of these illustrations, can confuse us. Another way of thinking about God is to consider love. For love to be complete it needs both someone to express it and someone to receive it. For God, who is love, to be complete He needs to exist in such a way that His love is expressed and received within Himself.

Don't worry too much if you are confused by all of this. On the contrary, why not give thanks that God is beyond our understanding?

Read Genesis 1:1–2, 26 and Matthew 3:16–17. Can you see all three persons of God in both of these passages? Note down your thoughts.

O———————————————————————————

O———————————————————————————

The Matthew passage shows us that Jesus needed to have the Holy Spirit before He began His work. So if Jesus needed the Holy Spirit then how much more do we need God's Spirit in order to be effective Christians?

In the passage in Genesis we saw that the Holy Spirit was hovering over the waters of the earth ready to be involved in the spectacular creation of the world. Could it be that the Holy Spirit is hovering over your community looking to do something spectacular in and through you?

So how does the Holy Spirit help you to become an influencer for Christ? Read the following passages and match them to the statements: John 16:8, Romans 8:16, Galatians 5:22–23, Acts 1:8, John 14:26 and Acts 4:8.

Verse   Passage

....   **The Holy Spirit tells us that we are members of God's family**
Genes prove that we are a direct member of a family, something that is in us and part of us. The Holy Spirit is God in us showing others and us that we are a part of God's family.

....   **The Holy Spirit transforms our character to become more like God**
The fruit of the Spirit describes what Christ is like. The Holy Spirit is at work in us to help us become more like Christ. The fruit is evidence of God's work in our lives.

....   **The Holy Spirit challenges us about the right way to live**
The Holy Spirit is like a conscience that measures what we're doing against God's standard for our lives. He tells us what we should and shouldn't do.

....   **The Holy Spirit helps us to remember what the Bible teaches us**
Most of us don't have a great memory but the Spirit of God enables us to understand and remember God's living word.

The Holy Spirit gives us boldness and courage to be effective witnesses

In Acts 4, Peter and John are hauled up in front of the religious leaders, who are very upset with what they are doing – healing people and sharing the gospel! A few months back Peter had denied Jesus – but this is a different Peter now. He's already spoken to thousands of people on the day of Pentecost. This verse reveals the source of Peter's boldness and courage.

The Holy Spirit gives us power

Before Jesus ascends to heaven, He clearly tells the disciples that the Holy Spirit will give them power to be effective witnesses across the whole world.

Pray for a minute and write down what you think the Holy Spirit would like to be doing in your community.

Empowering Christians

Holy Spirit

Underline anything that you think the Holy Spirit is already doing.

God is everywhere but we are promised more specifically that He is in us. Don't spend your time looking in the early morning fog for the Spirit of God. Look within yourself. When you became a Christian God put His Holy Spirit in you from the word 'go' – see John 14:17 and 1 Corinthians 6:19.

But even though we have the Spirit we can be greedy for more of God. The verse we read at the beginning of this session from Ephesians 5:18 would actually be better translated as '. . . be continually filled with the Holy Spirit'.

So how can we ensure that the Holy Spirit's impact is continually growing in our lives?

Read Luke 11:9–13 and summarise the answer that Jesus gives to this question.

○ ————————————————————————

○ ————————————————————————

Got it! The key message is that we should ask . . . and keep on asking . . .

So the message here is that just as the Holy Spirit was there before God created the world, He is still here. He lives within you and is at work in your community. Do you believe it? We need to remember though that our inactivity can seriously limit His action. How would your friends react if they knew God is at work within the community? Jesus suggested that they probably wouldn't believe because for them 'seeing is believing'. They may never see the Spirit, but they might experience Him through you. That's where you can play a part.

Get active!
Why not pray and ask God for more of His Spirit?

influencers 3. Spirit Empowered

Now make a list of all the things you'd like to do but need the Holy Spirit to help you do.

○————————————————————————————

○————————————————————————————

Talk to your mentor, show them your list and ask them to suggest some areas that they think the Holy Spirit is wanting to change. Now pray together for this to happen.

To finish, turn to 'Your Key Learning Points' and write down a few sentences to summarise the key things that you have learned from this session.

Session 4
Knowing the Father

Session aim:

The aim of this session is to help you understand the nature of God as Father, and to understand why His fatherhood is so important for your Christian walk.

Get motivated!

How do you feel about the fact that God wants to be your heavenly Father?

Perhaps you're wondering why God is Father? Let's look at some scriptures to help us understand this.

Read Genesis 1:1; 27 and Isaiah 66:1-2. What are the key messages of these passages?

These scriptures point out to us that God is the Father of all creation. He created the world and everything in it – and that includes you! He has no favourites and He is deeply concerned with all His creation. There *are* some things that He values though!

Read Isaiah 66:2b and write in your own words what God values.

O————————————————————————————

O————————————————————————————

This amazing God loves all of His creation, but He's particularly looking for humble people who will love Him and His word. Humility is not about thinking you are rubbish and everyone else is better. Being humble is about:

- Recognising and valuing your strengths and weaknesses
- Recognising that you're not better than anyone else – we're all equal in God's sight
- Recognising that God is God – and we should trust Him in everything.

So what kind of Father do you think God is? Write down some words that describe what you think God is like.

....

....

....

If God is our heavenly Father how should we act towards Him?

O————————————————————————————

influencers 4. Knowing the Father

The Bible is full of suggestions as to the best way to treat God – and it's not always easy. However, it's a great comfort to know that even when we do mess up, God still loves us and is always faithful. Jesus told a story to help us understand this – a story that illustrates how God responds to us as Father.

Read this famous story, 'The Prodigal Son', in Luke 15:11–31 and then choose the box below which represents the response that the father had in the story.

1. When the son asks for his share of the inheritance up front, effectively wishing the father dead, the father responds by:

   ○ Punishing the son for such disrespect

   ○ Being generous and showing mercy to the son by giving him what he does not deserve

2. When the father discovers that the son has wasted all the money, the father responds by:

   ○ Getting angry and commenting on how hopeless the son is

   ○ Being patient, knowing that we all make mistakes

3. When the father discovers that the son has nothing but the clothes on his back, and has a job feeding pigs, the father responds by:

   ○ Gloating that the son is only getting what he deserves

   ○ Offering unconditional love

continued . . .

influencers 4. Knowing the Father

4. When the son finally returns asking for a job as a servant in his father's house, the father responds by:

○ Giving him the lowest servant job out of revenge

○ Celebrating his return as a son

Those who heard this story would have been shocked by the response of the father. Jesus' hearers would have expected the father to respond with anger, with a desire to punish and take revenge upon the son in response to his appalling behaviour. If we're honest, we can sometimes believe that God is like this with us. We find it easier to believe that God is angry and looking for ways to punish us.

But Jesus tells this parable to describe what God is really like as a Dad. We might reject Him, wanting to rule and run our own lives, believing we know better than Him. Yet all the time He's waiting for us to come back to Him – wanting us to return. God's there with arms open wide wanting to accept us and love us for who we are. He's an incredible Dad!

Psalm 103:8–12 offers a fantastic description of Father God. Read this now and note particularly the four things that verse 8 says about the nature of God.

1. ....

2. ....

3. ....

4. ....

How would you want to respond to a Father like this?

Before we move off this parable there are two important questions that we need to consider.

First, if God's love is so unconditional does that mean He doesn't mind what we do?

◯ Yes   ◯ No

In the story of the prodigal son the father unconditionally accepted his son. However, we cannot draw from this that he unconditionally agreed with what the son had done. The truth is that God loves us but He can hate some of the things we do. The reason He hates some of our actions (sin) is because He knows that such things ultimately hurt us, other people and our relationship with Him.

Secondly, if God's love is so unconditional does that mean we never need to change?

◯ Yes   ◯ No

God wants the best for us and that means He wants us to live life His way – which is the best way. God may be full of mercy and grace, slow to anger and rich in love, but this doesn't give us the right to walk all over Him. In fact, because He is so amazing we should want to follow Him and be the best that we can be for Him.

Hopefully you're getting a good picture of the kind of father God is. There's something that we all need to remember though . . . God is not our fairy godmother! Too often we stick God next to Santa Claus and the tooth fairy. We talk to Him when we need something and assume that He always wants what we want. But that's not necessarily true. God doesn't always give us what we want, but that doesn't mean that He doesn't love us. The

Match up the verses with the correct statements by drawing a line to connect them.

Proverbs 3:12   The Father makes us His children

Matthew 6:26   The Father delights in us

Zephaniah 3:17   The Father disciplines us for our good

John 1:12   The Father provides for us

Father knows what is best for us – and what's best may not be what we think! Equally, He wants to help us grow into people who care and give, rather than those who are selfish and take.

Read Job 38, but brace yourself. It's about God being fed up with us second guessing Him. He is loving. He is our friend. Yet He is also immensely powerful and He can do anything He likes.

Write your own version of Job 38, listing all the things that God can do that we can't. As you write it, give thanks to God for how huge, powerful and incredible He is. Choose three lines that you really like and write them in the box provided.

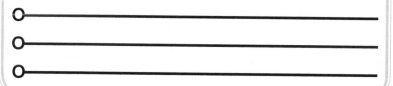

As this session comes to a close, write down the most important thing you've learned about God as Father in this session.

○————————————————————————————————

○————————————————————————————————

Remember that the Father is for you, not against you. Nothing you can do can make Him love you more or less. He loves you because He loves you and He longs for you to have the most fulfilling life through knowing Him. Our only response to such love should be to follow and obey Him.

Get active!

For some people this is the hardest part of Christianity. They find the idea of God as a good Father very difficult to accept. Some find it very normal.

This week talk to your friends about how your views on God have changed through reading *Influencers*. Remember they may not believe the same things as you, so respect their views. Listen to their views and share some of your own.

To finish, turn to 'Your Key Learning Points' and write down a few sentences to summarise the key things that you have learned from this session.

Session 5
Kingdom Living

Session aim:
The aim of this session is to help you understand what the kingdom of God is, and the role you have within it.

Get motivated!
Imagine a world where God's will is always done; a place where Jesus rules. This is the kingdom of God.

> **In your own words, build a picture of what you think the kingdom of God is like.**
>
> ○——————————————————
> ○——————————————————

Before we work out when and where the kingdom of God is, we need to work out what it is.

Every kingdom has a king. The kingdom of God is where Jesus is King. It is a place where everything that *He* wants happens.

Every king is treated as king. In the kingdom of God, Jesus is treated with respect; He is followed, obeyed and revered.

Every king is trusted and obeyed. In God's kingdom we trust Him to know best, and we follow and serve Him because He has our best interests at heart.

43

Every king gives his subjects what they need. God's kingdom is advancing, and it moves through Jesus working through us. He doesn't leave us to extend His kingdom alone; He gives us what we need to do the job.

So where is this kingdom? Jesus was once asked this question. Read Luke 17:20–21 to see His reply. Where did Jesus say the kingdom was?

O————————————————————

The biggest difference between God's kingdom and the ones we experience on earth is that His kingdom is a *kingdom of the heart*. It is a place of free choice where we choose to let God become King of our lives. The kingdom of God is wherever people choose to let Jesus be King.

The kingdom of God is mentioned 65 times in the New Testament, nearly every time by Jesus. It would be fair to say that He was obsessed with it.

Look at Mark 1:15. Remember that we have just read in Luke 17:20–21 that Jesus said the kingdom was within us. In Mark 1:15 Jesus says that the kingdom is:

O————————————————————

Jesus seems to be saying in these scriptures that the kingdom is 'now here' but also 'not yet here' (it's just near). What do you think He means by this?

O————————————————————

O————————————————————

The kingdom being 'now and not yet' is actually a key message of Jesus. It might sound confusing but actually it makes sense. The kingdom of God is at work 'now' in the sense that God is living through Christians today. But at present the whole world does not recognise that Jesus is King. While on earth we have a small taste of what it is like for Jesus to rule and reign in our lives, but when we get to heaven we will experience the full deal.

The big challenge is whether we're willing to let Jesus rule and reign in our lives – whether we're willing to be used by God to see His kingdom break out wherever we go. How do you feel about that challenge?

O————————————————————————

O————————————————————————

So what does it mean to be a kingdom person?

Read Matthew 5:13–16. In this passage Jesus is saying that Christians extend the kingdom through being:

....   and   ....

Write down the uses of salt and light below.

The purpose of salt is to. . .
....
....
....

As a kingdom person I should be like salt by. . .
....
....
....

The purpose of light is to. . .
....
....
....

As a kingdom person I should be like light by . . .
....
....
....

influencers 5. Kingdom Living

Jesus warns us not to become like everyone else, but to stay different – deliberately different. If we don't, then what use are we to people? People need Christians to be different. If we don't remain different, then we move outside of God's best purposes for us. In fact the scripture in Matthew tells us that we become relegated to the place of being trampled on by the rest of humanity. Why? Because an ineffective Christian misses out on both the fullness of a Christ-like life and the empty satisfaction of a godless life. So Jesus tells us to shine, and hints at the glory of a 'shining salty' life. Jesus says that people will see our good deeds (verse 16) and they will in turn praise God.

What good deeds could you do so that people around you will praise God?

O _____

O _____

Think about it. Through your attitudes and actions, your 'salti-ness', you can cause people to praise God. Alternatively people who are rebelling against God can find your light exposes their darkness, causing a negative reaction.

Be prepared: sometimes people can say horrible things. Has this happened to you? If so write down what happened.

O _____

O _____

The kingdom of God is sometimes a reference to heaven, but more often than not it is a reference to a place where God's 'will' starts to be obeyed.

influencers 5. Kingdom Living

What do you think is God's will for your school or college?

○ ————————————————————————————

○ ————————————————————————————

God's kingdom isn't just about what He does – it is also what He wants. It is where exactly what God wants happens. A helpful way of looking at the kingdom of God is to see what it includes and what it doesn't.

Read the following verses and see if you can extract the references to kingdom activities and activities that are opposite to the way things should be done in the kingdom:

Romans 12:9–21; Ephesians 5:3–21; Colossians 3:1–17; 1 Corinthians 13:4–7; Ephesians 4:17–5:2; Philippians 2:1–11; Galatians 5:6–26; 1 Thessalonians 4:1–12

Kingdom activity	Opposite activity
....	....
....	....
....	....
....	....
....	....
....	....
....	....

Have a look at what you've written above. The kingdom of God can be a hard place to be. It may mean that we shouldn't do some of the things that we do and we should do some of the things we don't do.

influencers 5. Kingdom Living

The important thing we *must* recognise is that we can't become a kingdom person by a sheer act of will. In Session 3 we looked at the fact that it is the Holy Spirit at work in us who is making us more like Christ and less like our old selves. We need to recognise our weakness and ask God for His help in becoming the people He wants us to be.

Get active!

Make plans for being salt and light in your community. Consider some of the following areas and how you can be salt and light in them. Discuss your thoughts with your mentor:

- Loving your parents
- Bullies in school
- Homework
- Gossip
- Serving others
- Having a positive attitude to yourself and your situation
- Things you do at parties
- Attitudes to the opposite sex
- What you do with your money
- Being a responsible steward of God's earth

Write a list of things that you could change which would mean you are doing more for the kingdom of God and less for the kingdom of yourself.

....
....
....
....
....
....

To finish, turn to 'Your Key Learning Points' and write down a few sentences to summarise the key things that you have learned from this session.

Session 6
The Ideal Influencer

Session aim:
The aim of this session is for you to see how God can use you individually and specifically through the gifts He has given you, rooted in a heart to serve people.

Get motivated!
It's surprising that Christians can sometimes seem boring and unenthusiastic. The Christian life should be the most fulfilling and exciting life to live.

Read Ephesians 1:4–6 and 1:11–16 and see if you can summarise what the apostle Paul is so excited about.

O————————————————————

O————————————————————

O————————————————————

Paul is making an amazing statement. We are chosen by God, part of His family and designed and destined to live a glorious life, making an impact in our world with His good news. Consider the fact that we are chosen for such a life by the almighty living God – the very same God who threw the stars into space and created the atom. Why would anyone ignore such an amazing destiny and instead just blindly follow the crowd?

49

Unfortunately some of us believe the truth with our heads, but remain unchanged in our hearts. This means that even though we *understand* what God has for us we often don't *experience* what God has for us.

> **What does it mean to you to be called, destined and chosen by God?**
>
> O———————————————————————
>
> O———————————————————————

So we need to understand that we will only be fully satisfied in life when we live out the destiny He has for us. A key to this is recognising that God has gifted each of us with talents and abilities, and He wants us to use those abilities for His glory.

> **Read Romans 12:6a. Which of the following statements are true?**
>
> ◯ Only some people have gifts and abilities
> ◯ Everyone has gifts and abilities
> ◯ Everyone has the same gifts and abilities
> ◯ We can be gifted in anything and everything
> ◯ We all have different gifts
>
> **Paul is pretty clear that everyone is gifted but that we also have different gifts. What gifts/talents/abilities do you believe God has given you? Chances are they're the things that you find the easiest and most enjoy. If you're not sure, ask God to show you.**
>
> O———————————————————————
>
> O———————————————————————

It's important for us to recognise and appreciate the fact that we are *all* gifted. God doesn't miss anyone out. An influencer knows what they are good at and they use that gift to make a difference in the place where God has put them.

How can you use the gifts you've identified to affect your community?

O————————————————————————

O————————————————————————

Write down two things you will try and do this week to make a difference to people in your school or college using your gift(s).

1. ....

2. ....

We've learned that each influencer is unique and special, gifted by God to do great things. But we're not to brag about our gifts and consider ourselves better than others. God gives us gifts to serve people. The ideal influencer recognises that he or she is ultimately a servant.

Who do we ultimately serve? Read Matthew 6:24 and Joshua 24:15.

O————————————————————————

O————————————————————————

What does Matthew 25:37–40 remind us about how we serve God?

O————————————————————————

O————————————————————————

Yes, ultimately we should have a heart to serve God, and the primary way we do this is by committing ourselves to serving other people. Serving others can be tough, particularly because we naturally might only want to help people we like. Unfortunately, the Bible doesn't let us off that easily.

> **Read Philippians 2:3–4. What does this passage tell us about our attitude to serving others?**
>
> O———————————————————————
> O———————————————————————

In order to be a good servant we need a right view of ourselves and other people. We shouldn't have a high attitude, thinking that we're better than everyone, and neither should we have a low attitude, thinking that we're not good enough to serve anyone. We know that God loves and accepts us and we should therefore be willing to love and accept others. How should we do that?

> **Read James 2:15–17 and 1 John 3:17. Which of the sentences below best summarises the main points of these passages?**
>
> ○ Be aware of the needs of other people – it's the thought that counts!
> ○ Meet the needs of the people when you can – faith without works is dead!

So an ideal influencer is someone who serves God by serving others, making a practical effort to meet their real needs.

Now think of some of your friends.

What help do they need?	How can you serve them?
....	....
....	....
....	....
....	....
....	....

So far we've considered some foundations for servanthood, but let's take a moment to describe some of the important characteristics of a servant.

Look up each of the passages below and connect the scripture with the statement about servant character:

A servant is faithful to God	Matthew 6:1–4
A servant is obedient	1 Peter 4:11
A servant has the right motives	Galatians 5:25
A servant serves wholeheartedly	John 14:15
A servant serves with God's strength	Luke 9:26
A servant is bold for God – willing to stand out	Ephesians 6:7–8
A servant is led by the Holy Spirit	1 Samuel 12:24
A servant is not ashamed of Jesus	Acts 4:29

Jesus is our ultimate example of what it means to be a servant. The Bible tells us that Jesus is the King of kings, Lord of lords, Prince of Peace and Mighty God. If anyone deserved to be served it's Him. And yet, when Jesus came to the earth 2,000 years ago, He did not come to be served – but to serve others.

Read what Paul has to say about the servant Jesus in Philippians 2:5–11. What key points would you make about Jesus from this passage?

1. ....

2. ....

3. ....

4. ....

This is a fantastic passage of Scripture, which tells us that though Jesus was God He was willing to give up His status and become the lowliest of servants – serving us to the point of death. As a result of His desire to humble Himself for our sakes, God the Father rewarded Him so that all would know that Jesus is Lord. If Jesus is willing to be a servant, then how much more should we be willing to serve others? We do this in the knowledge that our serving will be rewarded – as we take care of others, God takes care of us.

influencers 6. The Ideal Influencer

Get active!

Take some time to ask God to help you grow in each of the following areas. Complete each of the sentences below.

I will seek to be more faithful to God by . . .

O————————————————————————

I will seek to be more obedient to God by . . .

O————————————————————————

I will ensure that I have the right motives when I serve people by . . .

O————————————————————————

I will ensure that I serve wholeheartedly by . . .

O————————————————————————

I will ensure that I am serving in God's strength by . . .

O————————————————————————

I will seek to be bold by . . .

O————————————————————————

I will seek to be led by the Holy Spirit in my service by . . .

O————————————————————————

I will have the courage not to be ashamed of Jesus by . . .

O————————————————————————

To finish, turn to 'Your Key Learning Points' and write down a few sentences to summarise the key things that you have learned from this session.

influencers 6. The Ideal Influencer

Counting the Cost

Session aim:

The aim of this session is to help you understand that there is a cost to following Jesus. We need to hold lightly to our hopes and dreams in the knowledge that God always knows best. Following Jesus and caring for others comes at a price but we do it to know the joy of serving Christ.

Get motivated!

Fill in the boxes below with what you think people dream for you in your future, e.g. to be a rock star, to go to university, to have four children:

You

Your parents

God

When we begin to lay down the top two boxes (our dreams and our parents' dreams) and allow God, through prayer, to begin

influencers 7. Counting the Cost

56

to change our outlook on life, *what God wants* begins to become *what we want*. So the more we get to know God, the more our hopes and dreams become like His. We need to recognise though that there is a cost to following God's vision for our lives.

Jesus once said some challenging words to a bemused crowd who were desperate to follow Him. Read Matthew 16:24–26 to see what He said. Summarise in your own words what you think Jesus was saying:

O———————————————————————

O———————————————————————

Ouch! That sounds hard and pretty painful. Have you ever wondered why we follow Jesus when He seems to only promise a hard life?

Anyone who thinks Christianity is boring is doing it wrong! True Christianity gets into every thought, motive, hope and dream. Too often we let it get into us 'a bit'; we enjoy it, but never let it near the hard places. For example, it's fine to have a really fun time with our friends at church, but when it comes to forgiving someone who has hurt us deeply, that's a different story. Too often Christianity loses its power because we only let Jesus into the nice places – not the places He wants to be.

List below any areas of your life where you think you have a 'Keep Out' sign (i.e. areas of your life you'd rather Jesus didn't challenge), e.g. Who owns your money? What about what you watch on TV?

....

....

....

....

What do you think it means to be totally 'submitted to God'?

If we're honest, most of us have stuff in our lives that is not fully submitted to God. There are some things we'd find very hard to sacrifice. Yet God does want us to fully submit everything to Him because He knows best. Nothing should be off limits – and that's costly.

Perhaps that's why Jesus talks about denying ourselves, taking up our cross daily and following Him. What do you think He means by this?

'Deny yourself' means.............................

'Take up your cross daily' means.............................

'Follow Me' means.............................

Denying yourself is not about thinking that you're rubbish or no good. It's about putting God and others first – working against the selfish culture we live in.

> Read Matthew 22:37–39, which tells us about three people we should love. Who are they?
>
> 1. ....
>
> 2. ....
>
> 3. ....

Taking up your cross daily speaks of being willing to make great sacrifices. The cross was the most painful death and none of us will probably ever physically need to suffer on a cross. But there are some sacrifices that we might have to make as we decide to follow Jesus.

> Can you think of sacrifices that you might need to make as you seek to pursue God?
>
> ○——————————————————————
> ○——————————————————————

Following Jesus challenges us to do what Jesus is doing, go where He is going, say what He is saying, etc.

influencers 7. Counting the Cost

Look at John 5:19. Who did Jesus say He was following?

○ _____

○ _____

We should have that same resolve of Jesus to only do what God is doing – to follow Him in all things.

Look at the following scriptures and summarise the key truth which should help us follow Jesus despite the cost:

Luke 6:22 ....

Romans 8:26 ....

1 Corinthians 15:58 ....

1 Peter 4:16 ....

So, following Jesus is the most exciting and rewarding pursuit for our lives, but it's not without cost. Jesus is very keen to ensure that we consider the cost up front. Look at what Jesus says about this in Luke 14:27–33.

Get active!

Write down in the space below what you think are the costs for you to follow Jesus at this time in your life.

The costs to me to follow Jesus at this time in my life are. . .

○ ———————————————————————————

○ ———————————————————————————

○ ———————————————————————————

Take some time to pray that God will encourage you and equip you in these areas.

To finish, turn to 'Your Key Learning Points' and write down a few sentences to summarise the key things that you have learned from this session.

Session 8
The Influencer

Session aim:

The aim of this session is to show how we have a leadership responsibility to bring godly influence to the world around us.

Get motivated!

In this box list all the words that you associate with the word 'leader':

....

....

....

....

Which of the following best describes you?

◯ A reluctant leader

◯ A keen leader

◯ Neither – you're not a leader

Some people struggle with the idea of being called a leader. The word 'leader' often conjures up negative images or abilities that we don't feel we can live up to. In order to get the right perspective on leadership we need to let some of those images go for the moment and approach leadership from a new perspective. No matter which box you ticked above, God's call to you is to influence this world, so let's begin to use the word 'influencer' instead. By the end of this session we hope you will be looking at how you can affect this world. Not in terms of your leadership, but in terms of your influence.

Write down the names of three people who have had significant influence on your life. How did they influence you?

Name	How did they influence you?	Was it positive or negative?
....	....	....
....	....	....
....	....	....

Now consider three people you influence today. How do you influence them? And is your influence positive or negative?

Name	How do you influence them?	Is it positive or negative?
....	....	....
....	....	....
....	....	....

The point of this exercise is to demonstrate that every one of us is influenced by others, and every one of us influences other people. The key challenge is to consider what kind of influence we will be.

63

Jesus was an incredible leader whose influence was amazing. People willingly gave up their lives, jobs and families to follow Him. His words and deeds inspired riots and royal behaviour. They turned paupers into princes and priests into peasants. His compassion melted the hardest hearts and His convictions

Read Matthew 23. Jesus tells the Pharisees why their poor behaviour is a bad influence. See if you can match the verses to the problem behaviour that Jesus mentions. Then look at the opposing right behaviour that we should be practising. Some of the words might be new to you but we've provided descriptions to help you understand them.

Verse	Problem behaviour	Right behaviour
15	Legalism	Grace
	They cared about keeping the law more than they cared about people	
16–22	Pride	Humility
	They considered themselves better than everyone else	
23	Complacency	Commitment
	They weren't concerned about telling people about the kingdom	
1–4	Irresponsible	Responsible
	They led people astray rather than properly discipling them in the kingdom	
5–7	Dishonesty	Honesty
	They deceived people and stretched the truth to serve their own purposes	
25–28	Compromise	Faithfulness
	They only obeyed the parts of God's law that they wanted to	
13	Hypocrisy	Integrity
	They pretended to be better followers of God than they were	

64

challenged the cleverest minds. He truly was the greatest influencer in human history! But what was it about Jesus that enabled Him to have such a great impact?

In contrast, the priests and Pharisees in Jesus' day generally did not have a positive influence on people. Jesus' toughest words were saved for those He felt should know better. He knew that God's people should be leading by example, positively influencing others through living and declaring the kingdom.

The Pharisees often had a negative influence because their lives were characterised by being legalistic, proud, complacent, irresponsible, dishonest, compromising and hypocritical. We will never bring a kingdom influence if we are like this. In contrast, the kingdom calls us to be people of grace, humility, commitment, responsibility, honesty, faithfulness and integrity.

Take some time now to consider each of these behaviours and identify an example in terms of avoiding the problem behaviour and encouraging right behaviour.

I will avoid legalism and demonstrate grace by:

O————————————————————

I will avoid pride and demonstrate humility by:

O————————————————————

I will avoid complacency and demonstrate commitment by:

O————————————————————

I will avoid being irresponsible and demonstrate responsibility by:

O————————————————————

continued . . .

I will avoid dishonesty and demonstrate honesty by:

○————————————————————————————

I will avoid compromise and demonstrate faithfulness by:

○————————————————————————————

I will avoid hypocrisy and demonstrate integrity by:

○————————————————————————————

By doing, or not doing, these things you're committing yourself to being a godly influence for the kingdom wherever you are – just like Jesus!

It's important for us to consider what specific things we can influence. There are some things that we can't really have a great deal of influence over, e.g. what time school starts. It's important that we have our eyes on the right things.

List some areas below where you think you can bring influence:

....

....

....

....

Get active!

What kind of influencer are you right now?

○ ━━━━━━━━━━━━━━━━━━━━━━━━━━━━━━━━━━━

○ ━━━━━━━━━━━━━━━━━━━━━━━━━━━━━━━━━━━

Consider what specific things you can say and do this coming week to bring a kingdom influence to the world. Why not identify specific people you can seek to positively influence?

Name of person	What will I seek to say and/or do?
....	....
....	....
....	....
....	....
....	....
....	....

Pray with your mentor that God will enable you to achieve influence.

To finish, turn to 'Your Key Learning Points' and write down a few sentences to summarise the key things that you have learned from this session.

influencers 8. The Influencer

67

The Shepherd

Session aim:
The aim of this session is to help us to understand the difference between shepherds and sheep. Which are we, and how will this affect all that we do and everyone we should influence?

Get motivated!
Jesus spent a lot of time talking about sheep. There were lots of shepherds in those days and many people would have understood the analogies He gave about shepherds and sheep. He also talked a lot about farming and fishing, which were equally familiar trades to people of that time.

A number of times Jesus referred to Himself as the shepherd. The most famous example of this is in John 10:1–18. Look at each of these statements and determine which are 'true' or 'false' compared with the passage:

	True	False
The shepherd knows the sheep by name	◯	◯
The shepherd lets the sheep do their own thing	◯	◯
The sheep follow the shepherd	◯	◯
The sheep recognise the voice of the shepherd	◯	◯
The shepherd will lay down his life for the sheep	◯	◯

continued . . .

What is the difference between sheep and the shepherd? Find out what you can about the different characters, e.g. sheep need everything done for them.

Sheep

....

....

....

....

Shepherd

....

....

....

....

Do you think God wants you to be a sheep or a shepherd?

◯ Sheep   ◯ Shepherd   ◯ Both

The correct answer is 'both'. Jesus wants you to be a sheep in the sense that you should be following Him, for He is the 'Good Shepherd'. Yet Jesus also wants you to have a shepherding responsibility for your friends at school – and even your enemies! The Christian shepherd's primary responsibility is to lead sheep (people who don't know Jesus) to Jesus, and care for them and support them along the way.

Name some people you would find it easy to shepherd:

....

....

....

....

....

....

Name some people you would find it difficult to shepherd:

....

....

....

....

continued . . .

influencers 9. The Shepherd

Read Matthew 18:12–14. Are we allowed to be selective in caring for some sheep but allowing other sheep to go their own way?

○ Yes   ○ No

The truth is that the shepherd cares for the well-being of *all* the sheep. Jesus is for everybody – even for people we might struggle with.

Now some of you might read this, take it to heart and then make a *big* mistake. The mistake would be to choose to be a leader in the traditional sense of the word. You might seek to become the answer to everyone's problems, telling people what to do, doing everything yourself and thinking that everything depends on you. All this does is to make other people dependent on you. Often the traditional leader can seem to become judgemental and self-righteous.

Jesus' model looks different. Jesus comes alongside us, seeking to guide and support us so that we can make the right decisions in life. He does not make those decisions for us but helps us to stay on the right path.

Name some practical ways in which you can help people think about following Jesus:

○ _____

○ _____

○ _____

○ _____

To summarise, being a good shepherd is about:

Helping and serving other people	◯ True	◯ False
Getting people to do what you want	◯ True	◯ False
Leading people to Jesus	◯ True	◯ False
Making yourself look good	◯ True	◯ False
Setting other people up for success	◯ True	◯ False
Helping people realise your goals	◯ True	◯ False
Helping people realise their goals	◯ True	◯ False

Get active!

Now work through the following list to identify what you could do to be a good shepherd for the following groups of people:

Who?	How?
Best friends	....
Youth group	....
Christian union	....
People in your class	....
Friends	....
Most bullied person in your year	....
People you dislike	....
Family	....
A lonely person	....
Teachers	....

influencers 9. The Shepherd

With your mentor look at your answers, and discuss and pray about the people who have come to your mind. Could it be that some of these people are the ones you've agreed to guide to safety (to Jesus)?

To finish, turn to 'Your Key Learning Points' and write down a few sentences to summarise the key things that you have learned from this session.

influencers 9. The Shepherd

Session 10
Learning through God's Discipline

Session aim:

In Session 4 we looked at the nature of God as Father. We talked briefly about the fact that one of God's roles as Father is that He disciplines us so that we can reach our potential. In this session we will be looking at this in more detail as we continue to learn and grow under His discipline.

Get motivated!

Learning often doesn't sound like fun. Discipline sounds even worse. It suggests punishment and lots of effort. It sounds unpleasant and painful. Sometimes it can be, but if we want to grow as Christians, then discipline is a reality.

> **Can you think of any positive discipline experiences?**
>
> ○ ——————————————————————————————
>
> ○ ——————————————————————————————

Discipline is about a chosen way of doing things. It's about making good choices which develop our character or fitness. God disciplines people through situations, experiences, prayer and the Bible.

It's really important that we understand we are profoundly loved by God. He wants to protect us, but He also wants us to become more like Jesus, to become who we were designed to be. His discipline brings this about.

Read Hebrews 12:5–11 and consider the following questions:

Why should we not feel discouraged when God disciplines us? (see verse 6)

O——————————————————————————————

What does God want to achieve through disciplining us? (see verse 10)

O——————————————————————————————

Are we supposed to enjoy God's discipline? (see verse 11)

O——————————————————————————————

What's the long-term benefit of God's discipline? (see verse 11)

O——————————————————————————————

Picture the scene. A father and his child are playing with a toy. The child keeps getting it wrong and the father is losing patience. The situation builds and builds. The father continues to give the child more opportunities to learn. Finally, it is all too much. The father gives up, snatches the toy from the child and does it himself. At that moment, the child cries and learns that the father is more interested in getting the toy working than in the child.

God is *not* like this. He is patient beyond measure and keeps allowing opportunities for us to learn. Never is the task so important that He would snatch it from us and do it Himself. Having said that, He may choose to get something done another way, while continuing His discipling agenda with us. Sometimes it might feel that His whole plan could be in jeopardy while He waits for us. Our learning and growth is vital to Him. He can appear hard on us, but His motives are unquestionable. God is always good. The problem is often that our perception of His goodness gets clouded by our momentary pain.

There are two main ways that God disciplines us:

1. God sometimes allows us to go through difficult experiences

Read Romans 5:3–4.

Paul says that we should rejoice in our sufferings because our struggle produces

.... **which produces**

.... **which produces**

....

Can you think of some difficult experiences you've been through in your life? What might God have been teaching you through these?

Difficult experience   **Through this, God has been teaching me about . . .**

....

....

....

....

We might find it hard to understand why God allows some things to happen to us. However, through these experiences God wants us to place our hope and trust in His love, knowing that He will bring us through and we will grow through the journey.

2. God allows us to face the consequences of our sin

The Bible is full of people who seemed unable to do what God had said was best – pretty much like us. Jesus' death and resurrection removes the consequences of sin from us in terms of being distant from God and dead in our spirit. However, sometimes there are still consequences we have to face on earth today when we mess up.

Can you think of something you've done wrong and what the consequences of this were?

O———————————————————————

O———————————————————————

Why do you think God sometimes allows us to face the consequences of our sin?

O———————————————————————

O———————————————————————

Read Galatians 6:7–10. If you had to sum this passage up, what would you say?

O———————————————————————

O———————————————————————

One of the key messages of this passage is that we reap what we sow. There are always consequences to our actions. We can sow good things or bad things.

Let's consider some examples to drive the point home. . .

If you had a problem with telling the truth and often lied to people (sowing lies) what do you think would be the consequences of this for your relationships, i.e. what might you reap?

O———————————————————————

O———————————————————————

If you took the time to help people (sowing goodness) what do you think would be the consequences of this, i.e. what might you reap?

O———————————————————————

O———————————————————————

Hopefully this will have helped you to see the truth of the saying 'You reap what you sow'. If you sow sinful acts you will reap the negative consequences. If you sow for God by seeking to please Him you will see some fruit on earth but also grow a storehouse in heaven.

Read Revelation 3:19–21.

What does God do?

O———————————————————————

Why?

O———————————————————————

What should our response be?

O———————————————————————

God lets us experience the good and the bad. He knows that we will develop character and discipline through these experiences. Often we look at the bad things that happen to us and believe they are the work of the devil. We look at the good things and believe they are from God. But maybe it isn't that black and white. Maybe God isn't like our fairy godmother, seeking to give us just what we want. Maybe He is like a loving father, protecting His children sometimes, but at other times letting us learn.

We need to understand that life is for living and living to the full. It is about risk and cost. It is also about joy and triumph. You don't get one without the other. Christian fullness comes when you hold the good in one hand, the bad in the other, and bring them together – appreciating God's loving discipline.

Get active!

With your mentor make a list of some of your good and bad experiences. Pray together about them, and ask God to help you learn from both, keeping a good attitude.

○———————————————————————
○———————————————————————
○———————————————————————
○———————————————————————
○———————————————————————
○———————————————————————

To finish, turn to 'Your Key Learning Points' and write down a few sentences to summarise the key things that you have learned from this session.

Session 11
Learning through Self-Discipline

Session aim:

In the last session we looked at the importance of learning by allowing God to lovingly discipline us. The aim of this session is to look at the importance of learning through self-discipline.

Get motivated!

List areas in your life where you have to exercise self-discipline, and say why this is important.

Self-discipline	Importance
....	....
....	....
....	....
....	....

The following areas are foundational for leading the Christian life: prayer, Bible reading, worship and community.
Let's look at each of these areas in turn.

> **How would you rate your self-discipline in these areas at this time?**
>
> | | | | | | | | |
> |---|---|---|---|---|---|---|---|
> | **Prayer** | ◯ Regular | ◯ Ad hoc | ◯ Rare | ◯ Never |
> | **Bible reading** | ◯ Regular | ◯ Ad hoc | ◯ Rare | ◯ Never |
> | **Worship** | ◯ Regular | ◯ Ad hoc | ◯ Rare | ◯ Never |
> | **Community** | ◯ Regular | ◯ Ad hoc | ◯ Rare | ◯ Never |

Prayer

Prayer is simply a conversation with God where both parties should be speaking and listening – but not at the same time! There are loads of different ways to pray, e.g. need prayers, help prayers, quiet times, intercession.

Praying doesn't come easily for most people. It's a discipline and sometimes we don't even know where to start. Our prayer

> **Write a list of all the types of prayer you can think of.**
>
> ....
>
> ....
>
> ....
>
> ....
>
> ....

times can include:

- Times of praise – thanking God for His goodness

- Times of forgiveness – asking God to forgive us for things we have done wrong
- Times of request – asking God for help in specific situations
- Times of listening – allowing God the opportunity to speak to us

Prayer isn't about getting God to do what we want. We should be changed through prayer as we invest time:

- declaring His greatness
- confessing our selfishness and sin
- calling out for our friends to know God and for God to extend His kingdom
- making space for Him to change us

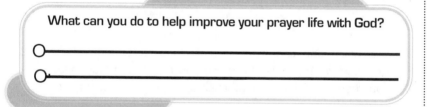

What can you do to help improve your prayer life with God?

Bible reading
Pick up your Bible. Look at it. The Bible is an amazing book. It's the only book in the whole history of the world that tells us how and why the world began, and how and why the world will end. Yet it's so much more than that!

influencers 11. Learning through Self-Discipline

Match the scriptures with the statements:

The Bible is God's 'living' word – it has the power to change things; it gets to the core of our being like a surgeon's knife

2 Peter 1:20–21

The Bible is God's 'inspired' word – written by men and women under the direction of the Holy Spirit

2 Timothy 3:16–17

The Bible is God's 'roadmap' for effective living – the creator informing the created about how to live

Hebrews 4:12

We often find the discipline of Bible reading hard. This is because we often read the Bible in the wrong way. Next time you read the Bible, ask yourself some of these key questions:

- What type of writing am I reading, e.g. story, law, poetry, prophecy?
- What did this passage mean for the people it was written for back then?
- What does the passage tell me about God?
- What does it mean for me today? How might I need to change in response to this?

Why not have a go at this now by reading Revelation 3:19–22 and answering those questions:

What type of writing am I reading?

O———————————————————————

What did this passage mean for the people it was written for back then?

O———————————————————————

What does the passage tell me about God?

O———————————————————————

What does it mean for me today?

O———————————————————————

How might I need to change in response to this?

O———————————————————————

Finally, remember that the Bible isn't just there for information. James tells us in James 1:22 that we should not just read or listen to it but. . .

O———————————————————————

Worship

There is something powerful in worshipping God. It takes our eyes off ourselves and focuses them on something bigger. As we focus on God our situations fall into perspective. We see more clearly. For some, worship is an obligation. For others, it is an experience. Whichever you are, God deserves it as a discipline in your life.

Which of these activities would you consider to be worship?

○ Drawing ○ Singing ○ Writing ○ Dancing

○ Reading ○ Working ○ Homework ○ Washing up

○ Tidying ○ Serving

The truth is that all of these can be worship if we do them to please God, using the gifts that He has given us. Worshipping God isn't just about singing; it's about offering our whole lives to Him.

Read Romans 12:1–2. What should we offer God in view of His love and mercy?

○ Our songs ○ Ourselves

Can you think of five great reasons why God is worthy of our worship?

1. ....

2. ....

3. ....

4. ....

5. ....

With all this in mind, how can you worship God in your school in different and creative ways?

○———————————————————————

○———————————————————————

influencers 11. Learning through Self-Discipline

Community

We were never designed to follow Jesus by ourselves. We need each other. The story of Adam and Eve proves this when God said that it wasn't good for Adam to be alone. When Jesus returned to heaven the early disciples knew that it was important that they met together regularly.

> **Look at Acts 2:42–47 and note down the kind of things that the disciples did together.**
>
> ....
>
> ....
>
> ....
>
> ....

The Bible tells us that as a result of this interdependent way of living loads of people became Christians every day (Acts 2:47). Wow! Imagine that!

> **The Bible gives us some clear indications of what else we're supposed to do when we come together in community. Can you match up the scriptures with the actions?**
>
> Confess our sins to each other   Colossians 3:13
>
> Support each other   James 5:16
>
> Forgive each other   Hebrews 10:24
>
> Encourage one another   Galatians 6:2
>
> Inspire one another   John 13:34–35
>
> Love one another   1 Thessalonians 5:11

Get active!

As a response to this session write down one thing you will do in the following week to develop your commitment in each of the four areas of self-discipline.

Prayer

O————————————————————————

Bible reading

O————————————————————————

Worship

O————————————————————————

Community

O————————————————————————

To finish, turn to 'Your Key Learning Points' and write down a few sentences to summarise the key things that you have learned from this session.

Session 12
Spread the Word!

Session aim:
This session looks at the importance of telling people about Jesus so that they have an opportunity to know Him.

Get motivated!
We might not recognise it, but humans are all designed with a natural need for God – a God-shaped space somewhere deep inside of us. It's empty due to our sin. Only God can fill the space. Unfortunately, most people won't just discover God by chance.

> **Read Romans 10:13–15. How will people come to believe in Jesus?**
>
> ○ ————————————————————————
>
> ○ ————————————————————————

If you take the risk to share with others what you have found, God can work in them. Each time God moves to forgive sin and to make them whole, we have the privileged role of being part of it. As we'll discover, the Bible tells us that we are all witnesses, i.e. people who tell others what Jesus has done for them. A witness tells others what they have seen. Our job is to tell others what we have seen God do.

Imagine that you happened to stumble across the cure for cancer. What would you do?

◯ Patent the idea and sell the cure

◯ Do everything in your power to cure people

◯ Not say anything

◯ Tell some of your friends who don't have cancer that you have the cure. Then form a club of people who know the cure but never actually cure anyone

◯ Bury the idea so no one finds out

You'd do everything in your power to cure people, right? (If you ticked the first answer, you need help.) The reality is that you have even better news than the cure for cancer. You know that the creator of the universe loves us so much that He allowed His own Son to die on the cross for our sins. You know that Jesus rose from the dead and is alive today, offering forgiveness, new life, hope and purpose for every man, woman and child. But what will you do with that news?

Imagine being with the disciples 2,000 years ago. You are gathered on a hill outside Jerusalem with the risen Jesus. He's talking to you. He has endured the cross, gone through all the suffering and is about to return to His Father. Jesus, your Lord, the centre of your attention, catches your eye and tells you what you should commit the rest of your earthly life to.

influencers 12. Spread the Word!

Read what Jesus said in Acts 1:7–9.

What does Jesus call us to be? ....

Where? ....

It doesn't take a genius to work out that people need hope and help today. God's response 2,000 years ago was to send Jesus to offer a new hope to a hurting world. God didn't just sit back – He got involved and decided to make a difference.

Take a moment to write down the names of three of your best friends and then write down the names of three people you sometimes struggle to get on with.

My friends	People I clash with sometimes
....	....
....	....
....	....

Now read 2 Peter 3:9. Does God want only our friends to know Him?

◯ Yes, we can't be expected to reach out to people we don't get on with

◯ No, God doesn't want anyone to miss out on His good news, so we should witness to everyone

What do you think a witness does?

○———————————————————

○———————————————————

Sometimes we're worried that God is expecting us to stand on street corners and shout at people as they walk past about how much God loves them. The truth is that very few of us will probably ever be called by God to do that and it's probably not what Jesus really had in mind. To be a witness for Jesus is simply to be willing to tell others about the difference that Jesus has made in your life. By witnessing you're telling the story about how you came to believe the truth about Jesus and why you feel it's the most important news for everyone to know.

Think about it! God wants to use you to change the eternal destiny of your friends and family by sharing the message of Jesus with them. How do you feel about that?

○————————————————————————

○————————————————————————

Of course, telling people about Jesus isn't always easy. Why can it be so hard sometimes to tell others what we believe? List five reasons.

1. ....

2. ....

3. ....

4. ....

5. ....

If the reason you find it hard is that you're scared of being rejected for what you believe, remember this: when you get shunned for trying to witness, it's not you who's being rejected; it's Jesus. The person who always feels the most hurt when people turn their backs or mock what you know to be true isn't you; it's Him.

Read Matthew 5:10–12 and consider the following questions.

Will everyone accept the message of Jesus?

○ Yes   ○ No

Are you the first person who has ever had their message rejected?

○ Yes   ○ No

The Bible is full of people who spoke out on behalf of God. Sometimes people responded positively to this and other times people gave them a really hard time.

Can you think of any people in the Bible who were witnesses for God and yet found their message rejected?

....

....

If you're still feeling terrified about the thought of telling people about Jesus, then here are some great promises to give you courage.

Link the promises to the scriptures below.

Jeremiah 29:11	God loves us
John 3:16	God is for us
Isaiah 66:13	Angels camp round us
Romans 8:31	God has plans for us
Matthew 28:20	The Holy Spirit is in us
John 14:17	Jesus is with us
Psalm 91:11	God comforts us

These passages should make us feel secure. This doesn't mean that everything will be easy, but we need to know *we are not alone.*

What more do we want? Is there any more? Often we ask ourselves, 'Will I ever feel up to this?' To be honest, who knows? But one thing is certain: God commands us to be His witnesses and we must be obedient, despite how we feel.

Read 1 Peter 3:15–16. In this passage Peter gives us some important principles about witnessing that we would do well to remember. He reminds us that:

1. We need to make sure that Jesus is .... of our lives.

2. We should .... be ready to give an answer for our hope.

3. Our response to people should always be .... and ....

4. Our .... should also serve as an example of Jesus living in us.

It's reassuring that Peter is reminding us to be ready to give an answer when people ask us about Jesus. This means that we shouldn't feel the pressure to throw Jesus into every conversation. We should always be asking the Holy Spirit to create opportunities for us to witness, but trying to ram Jesus into every conversation will generally be unhelpful. It's important that we are gentle and respectful with people too. We need to take time to hear their own story and thoughts and not rubbish their opinion. Jesus always took time to listen to people, although He sometimes challenged people's opinions. (Think, for example, about how He reacted to the Pharisees on occasion.)

Finally, in this passage Peter reminds us that our behaviour should also be a good witness. Good witnesses speak of Jesus through their words *and* actions. Words without actions are empty. Some of us lean towards being 'a good Christian', e.g. being a nice person, while others of us lean towards talking a good talk, but not living it. Both on their own are wrong. The key is that we proclaim Jesus through words and actions. Saying it and living it. Only then can people see that the life Jesus offers is worth living and is effective.

What sort of things can you do to demonstrate your Christian faith?

O ——————————————————————

O ——————————————————————

influencers 12. Spread the Word!

Get active!

How are you feeling about sharing your faith? What has the material in this session made you think?

O————————————————————————

O————————————————————————

Can you think of the names of specific people you would like God to create an opportunity for you to witness to?

O————————————————————————

O————————————————————————

To finish, turn to 'Your Key Learning Points' and write down a few sentences to summarise the key things that you have learned from this session.

Session 13
Shout It Out!

Session aim:

In the last session we looked at the responsibility we have to be witnesses for Jesus through sharing our story. In this session we'll take time to clearly understand the answer to the question 'What is the good news about Jesus?'

Get motivated!

Look at the following statements. Which do you think are true and which are false?

Snails can sleep for up to four years   ◯ True   ◯ False

No piece of paper can be folded in half more than seven times   ◯ True   ◯ False

Donkeys kill more people annually than plane crashes do   ◯ True   ◯ False

It is possible to lead a cow upstairs, but not downstairs   ◯ True   ◯ False

A duck's quack doesn't echo and no one knows why   ◯ True   ◯ False

It's physically impossible for you to lick your elbow   ◯ True   ◯ False

Our eyes are always the same size from birth, but our nose and ears never stop growing. SCARY!   ◯ True   ◯ False

95

In fact, all of the above statements are true and yet none of them will really change your life. As Christians we believe the truths about Jesus are life-changing and so we want to make sure that people know the truth. After all, it was Jesus who said that when people know the truth, the truth will set them free.

If one of your friends came up to you and asked what the good news of Jesus is, what would you say? What points would you include in your message to them?

O————————————————————————————————

O————————————————————————————————

O————————————————————————————————

O————————————————————————————————

Did you find that exercise difficult? Sometimes it is difficult for us to say what we believe. For this reason, we're going to take some time to explore the essential good news message.

Read Genesis 1:27, Deuteronomy 32:6, Psalm 139:13–16 and Acts 17:28, and summarise below the key message from these passages:

Key message 1:

O————————————————————————————————

These passages tell us clearly that God created us. We only exist because of Him. The very breath in our body is an act of His creative power. The human body is incredibly complex. It takes more faith to believe we were evolved by chance. We believe that we were creatively and intentionally designed.

> Read Isaiah 54:10, Romans 8:38–39, Ephesians 3:17–19 and 1 John 4:10, and summarise below the key message from these passages:
>
> Key message 2:
>
> O———————————————————————

God didn't just create us. He loves us with an unquenchable love. He doesn't love us because we love Him. He doesn't love us because we're good people and do what He says. He loves us because He is our heavenly Father and love is part of His very nature. This is a really important message for people to know today. A lot of people think that God is distant and uncaring, or that He is angry and wants to get us. This is not the God of the Bible. We discovered what God is really like when we looked at the father nature of God in Session 4.

> Read Psalm 33:1, Jeremiah 29:11 and Romans 12:2, and summarise below the key message from these passages:
>
> Key message 3:
>
> O———————————————————————

The God who created and loves us doesn't stop there. He is passionately interested in every detail of our lives. In fact, these passages tell us clearly that God has great plans for our lives. Surely the one who created us knows what is best for us. God's plans for our lives exist so that we will have a fulfilling life both now and for all eternity. This doesn't mean that life will never be tough, but it does mean that we have God leading and guiding our path through the joy and trouble.

> **Read what Jesus had to say in John 10:10. In this passage He reveals the two agendas that there are for everybody in the world.**
>
> The agenda of the thief (Satan) is ....
>
> The agenda of Jesus is ....

> **Read Isaiah 53:6a, Romans 3:10, Romans 3:23, Romans 8:7–8 and 1 John 1:8, and summarise below the key message from these passages:**
>
> **Key message 4:**
>
> ————————————————————————

This is the tragedy of life today. The God who created us longs to pour out His love on us and enable us to enjoy His very best life. But we are all sinners – we've decided to make up our own rules and reject God. A simple explanation of sin is that it's doing your own thing, not the God thing. Thinking you know better than God, you run your life your own way, not His. God is perfect but we're not, and our sin gets in the way of our relationship with God and everything He has for us. There are serious consequences for us, both for now and for eternity, if we keep rejecting God.

What do you think the consequences are now? (See Ecclesiastes 2:11)

O——————————————————————————————

O——————————————————————————————

What do you think the consequences are for eternity? (See John 3:16; 25:46)

O——————————————————————————————

O——————————————————————————————

If people reject God while they're on the earth they'll miss out on fulfilling the dreams and plans of God for which they were born. Life will never be as fulfilling as it could be, as they'll always be wondering what the purpose of life is. People will only ever feel secure when they are living in relationship with their creator.

But it doesn't stop there. You get to keep what you die with! If people decide to reject God in this life they get to keep that decision for eternity. The Bible tells us that there are only two places to spend eternity – with God or without Him. Heaven and hell are often taboo subjects. We like to think that everyone will go to heaven and that hell doesn't exist. We can't imagine a God who sends people to hell. The truth is that God doesn't send anyone to hell – they decide to go by deciding to reject Him, and it breaks God's heart because He longs for everyone to be with Him. '

So there is a problem! Our sin gets in the way of our relationship with God, both now and for all eternity. But God has the solution.

influencers 13. Shout It Out!

> **Read Isaiah 53:5, John 3:16, Romans 5:6–8 and 1 Peter 3:18, and summarise below the key message from these passages:**
>
> **Key message 5:**
>
> O———————————————————————————

Yes! God proves His love for us by allowing His own Son to die on the cross for our sins. But Jesus proves that He is God's Son by rising from the dead three days later and as a result, the work of the cross and the grave gives us the opportunity to be fully reconciled with God. We can be forgiven, receive eternal life and discover God's great purpose for our lives. So how do we receive this?

> **Read Acts 3:19, Romans 10:9–13 and 1 John 1:9, and summarise below the key message from these passages:**
>
> **Key message 6:**
>
> O———————————————————————————

It couldn't be simpler really. We just ask God to forgive us and invite Him into our lives. To repent means that we turn from living life our way to living life God's way – we make God the boss of our lives because we recognise that He is our awesome creator God who knows what is best for us. We surrender our lives to Him.

> **In the light of everything we've talked about why do you think people should become Christians?**
>
> O———————————————————————————
>
> O———————————————————————————

influencers 13. Shout It Out!

Despite this, some people find witnessing really hard. There are lots of skills and tips on offer, but to be honest, there really are only three ways to get going:

- Get more passionate and focused on God, so that your every action and thought comes from Him. You'll be so excited about God that you won't be able to keep quiet.
- Grit your teeth. Remember you're doing people a favour, and at the right moment tell them about the Jesus you love, and how He feels about them.
- Take time to get to know people and genuinely care for them. As you grow to love people more, like God does, you'll know that Jesus is the very best thing for them.

Which tip suits you most?

O _____

O _____

Get active!

Why not take five minutes to summarise in your own words what the key message of the gospel is?

O _____

O _____

O _____

O _____

continued . . .

influencers 13. Shout It Out!

How do you feel about these truths?

O———————————————————————————

O———————————————————————————

O———————————————————————————

O———————————————————————————

To finish, turn to 'Your Key Learning Points' and write down a few sentences to summarise the key things that you have learned from this session.

influencers 13. Shout It Out!

Session 14
Helping People on Their Journey

Session aim:
In this session we look at how we can help people as they move towards God.

Get motivated!
You may have some friends and family members who just don't seem interested in Jesus at all – or perhaps you know people who are interested in Jesus but don't seem able to follow Him. It's as if people are sometimes stuck – they can't escape the life they're in and they see no way out. By now, if you've been talking about Jesus, behaving like Jesus and caring for people like Jesus, then people *will* have been affected. You may have even talked about sin, the cross and how Jesus can save them, and yet perhaps you're frustrated because nothing seems to be happening.

> **Why do you think your friends have so far decided against following Jesus?**
>
> ○ _____
>
> ○ _____

What we have to recognise is that people are at different stages in their journey towards God. It's not helpful simply to divide the population into those who are 'in' and those who are 'out'.

Read Psalm 84:5 (preferably in an NIV version of the Bible). Can you summarise what the key message of this passage is?

○ ——————————————————————

○ ——————————————————————

This passage is a good reminder that faith is a journey – a pilgrimage. All of us are journeying, including Christians, and at any point in time we are usually moving towards God or away from Him. Look at the scale below. Imagine that the number 1 represents the furthest point that someone can be away from following Jesus – they don't believe in God and don't care to find out about Him. The opposite end of the scale, 5, represents someone who is sold out for Jesus and really wanting to go on with God.

Take a moment to position your name on the scale to indicate where you are on your faith journey. It would also be good to write down the names of one or two people against each of the other stages to help you think about where different people are in their own faith journey.

1	2	3	4	5
....	....	....	....	....
....	....	....	....	....
....	....	....	....	....

The point of this exercise is to get you to recognise the journey of faith. The challenge is twofold. First, we need to ensure that we are personally moving in the right direction. Secondly, we need to consider how we can help others move on to their next stage and get closer to Jesus.

Can you think of some things that you can do to encourage people to move on in their faith journey? Consider the following scenarios:

What might you do to encourage someone who has no interest in God to start to consider Him?

O————————————————————————

What might you do to encourage someone who has started to show an interest in God and wants to find out more?

O————————————————————————

What might you do to encourage someone who knows that the good news about Jesus is true?

O————————————————————————

What might you do to encourage someone who has made a decision to follow Jesus?

O————————————————————————

What might you do to encourage someone who is passionate about following Jesus, whatever the cost?

O————————————————————————

We can't treat everyone the same. You wouldn't feed solid food to a newborn baby. Even the apostle Paul recognised this. Look at what he wrote in 1 Corinthians 3:1–3.

So if we want to help people move on with God the first challenge is to take time to recognise where they are and what we can do as a first step to help them move on.

One of the things you could do to help people move on in their faith is to try and introduce them to other believers, encouraging them to come to your church or youth group. How do you feel about that idea?

○ Great – my church and youth group are good

○ Nervous – they might laugh and tell me to get lost

○ No way – my church and youth group are pretty lame. It would make things worse

Sometimes we don't reach out because we are not proud of our church and don't want friends to 'suffer' it. For whatever reason, we see a situation we don't want to go near; we just want to avoid it. But the truth is that no church is perfect and if we are ashamed of our Christian community, then we are preventing our friends from getting God-intended help.

Fill in the following box, listing at least four friends you would love to come to church, youth group or a discovery group, and then fill in what keeps you from *regularly* inviting them.

Name	Reason for not *regularly* inviting them
....	....
....	....
....	....
....	....
....	....

Having just written down some reasons why you don't regularly invite your friends to church let's look at how you can address some of those reasons.

Divide your reasons up into the following groups.

Because they will or have already reacted badly	Because I like having my Christian and non-Christian groups separate	Because my church or group would put them off
....	....	....
....	....	....
....	....	....
....	....	....
....	....	....

Now work out some ways to get around these reasons. Remember, you're either part of the problem or part of the solution.

Because they will or have already reacted badly	Because I like having my Christian and non-Christian groups separate	Because my church or group would put them off
....	....	....
....	....	....
....	....	....
....	....	....
....	....	....

How can you make these changes happen?

O⎯⎯⎯⎯⎯⎯⎯⎯⎯⎯⎯⎯⎯⎯⎯⎯⎯⎯⎯⎯⎯⎯⎯⎯⎯⎯

O⎯⎯⎯⎯⎯⎯⎯⎯⎯⎯⎯⎯⎯⎯⎯⎯⎯⎯⎯⎯⎯⎯⎯⎯⎯⎯

Get active!

Having completed this session, what two things can you do to help your friends move on in their faith journey?

1. ....

2. ....

If you're concerned that your friends won't come to your church, think about the kind of church they might come to. What would it look like? Talk to your leader about the possibility of running something specially for them.

To finish, turn to 'Your Key Learning Points' and write down a few sentences to summarise the key things that you have learned from this session.

Session 15
How 2

Session aim:

In this session we aim to help you to develop and implement a vision for establishing a Christian group and activities specifically in your school or college.

Get motivated!

Throughout this programme we've been considering what God could do in your school or college through one willing believer – you! Now imagine God gathering lots of willing, active believers into one place. Imagine them agreeing on, and hungering after, a vision – a heavenly dream for their school.

> Read Ecclesiastes 4:9. What does this passage tell us about why it's good to work together with other people?
>
> ○ ———————————————————————
>
> ○ ———————————————————————

The bottom line here is that we can achieve so much more for the kingdom when we work together as opposed to working by ourselves. In the last session we looked at the challenge of encouraging your friends to move on in their faith journey, including looking at them coming to your church or youth group. We ended with the challenge to bring church to them. You, and other believers in your school, could do this by starting a Christian group in your school. Whether you call it a Christian Union

(CU), club, group or outreach is not important – the important thing is to get something started. Setting up a Christian group in school is taking up the challenge of putting together an organised group of influencers to which people can belong.

> **Schools need an established Christian community for:**
>
> - **Support – why?**
> ○————————————————————————
> - **Mission – why?**
> ○————————————————————————
> - **Prayer – why?**
> ○————————————————————————

Support – Schools can often be hostile environments. You can find yourself under pressure to do things that are not part of God's design. Gathering with other Christians can provide support, accountability and encouragement.

Mission – Schools might be hostile, but we are still meant to be missionaries. This means that as we go about our learning and socialising, we also have another agenda. We have a heavenly agenda: mission. This means we join in Jesus' obsession. What was that? To help people 'repent and believe the kingdom of God is near'. *To see His kingdom extended.* When Christians gather together in school, mission should be one of the things we discuss and do.

Prayer – This seems obvious but too often prayer can be forgotten. Remember, as a group of Christians we have God's ear. He promises to listen to our prayers. Too often we can believe too much in the power of people and forget the power of prayer. As Christians in school we gather not only to 'do' but also to 'pray'.

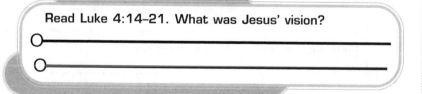

What is your current experience of a Christian group in school? If you have a Christian group in your school, answer the question below.

Why does it gather?

○ ────────────────────────────────────

○ ────────────────────────────────────

Any organised group of people needs a clear expression of vision and a list of values. Vision and values are the things that hold people together and provide a way of journeying together to a common goal in the future.

Developing vision

A vision is a picture of the future which guides the choices you make along the way. Vision creates purpose and direction. A Christian vision is God-orientated. It is helpful to express the vision in a sentence or a statement which is easy to communicate. An example of a vision from a Christian group in school is: '*Through prayer and holy demonstrative lives, this group intends to work together to see the kingdom of God expand in our school.*'

Read Luke 4:14–21. What was Jesus' vision?

○ ────────────────────────────────────

○ ────────────────────────────────────

Jesus had a very clear vision for His time on the earth. He knew what He was seeking to do and that gave focus to how He spent His time. If the Son of God needed a clear vision, then how much more do we?

influencers 15. How 2

111

> Have a go at writing a vision for your group with the other leaders.
>
> ○ ————————————————————————————
> ○ ————————————————————————————
> ○ ————————————————————————————
> ○ ————————————————————————————

Developing values

A value is a principle or belief that you are passionate about. Values influence how we achieve our vision. Our values motivate our activities.

Some great group values Jesus taught were:

- Love God
- Love each other
- Love the lost

> Your values will affect your actions. Consider the three values above and identify what actions will result from you living the values. We've given you a head start below.
>
> **Love God**   Bible reading
> ....
> ....
>
> **Love each other**   Not gossiping
> ....
> ....
>
> **Love the lost**   Inviting non-Christians
> ....
> ....

If these ideas interest you, read a great book called *The D Factor* by Liz West and Paul Hopkins. It will really help you understand how to live a more effective life.

Have a go at writing down some values for your group.

○ ——————————————————————————

○ ——————————————————————————

So now you've got a vision and some values for your group. What do you do now? Here are some ideas that will help you along.

- **A willing teacher** – Groups in schools need to have a teacher who is responsible for their actions. Make sure the teacher is happy with what you intend to do. It is also good to agree how much they will supervise you and whether they will attend the group. Most schools ask the teachers to be present at groups they look after. Make sure you discuss this at the very beginning. We suggest your teacher doesn't need to attend, but that they do meet regularly with the leaders in a supervisory role.

  Teacher's name: ....

- **An available room** – This room needs to be available all year.

  Room: ....

- **A good team** – You need other Christians who are willing to organise a group in your school. Make sure you find a team of people who know what they are setting out to do (a vision). It will save problems later. Make sure they are willing to learn the skills needed. Before you pick your team have a look at Session 8 again.

Team members: ....

....

....

....

- **Promotional material** – To let people know about the group, you could produce posters that give information about the group, including start date, time and room.

- **Assemblies** – Why not ask if you can take an assembly in your school? Remember these key principles:

  - Prepare the assembly
  - Keep it within the time boundary
  - Make it age specific, e.g. don't play silly games to recruit sixth formers
  - Remember you are advertising, not trying to convert people
  - Make it fun and interesting

  There are loads of good resources for assembly ideas to be found in your local Christian bookshop.

- **Get outside input** – Talk to the youth leaders in your area, and ask if you can visit their youth groups and advertise your new group.

- **Plan your programme** – Take time to consider what you will do in the group when it meets. Here are some ideas that you could include – and you could simply adapt some of the material from this *Influencers* programme:

  - Discovering gifts. All Christians have (are) gifts given by God for the common good. These need to be discovered. Why shouldn't it happen in the place where they can be used the most?
  - Identity. Many Christians are so affected by their environment that realising their God-given identity is a very difficult thing. Imagine the effect of Christians realising their identity in schools.

influencers 15. How 2

- Kingdom of God. If Jesus was obsessed with it, then we should be also. We should be exploring as a group what Jesus' kingdom looks like in our schools.
- What is the gospel? Too often the gospel is not understood by Christians. Why not teach what it is so that no one is confused by the Christians in your school?
- Evangelism. If evangelism is the job Jesus left us with, then it needs to be on the agenda of any group of Christians that meet together.

Get active!

Take some time to consider what your first steps will be to launch a new Christian group in your school. Summarise your vision and values for establishing the group, and specify who can help you and how you plan to get started.

○———————————————————
○———————————————————
○———————————————————
○———————————————————
○———————————————————
○———————————————————
○———————————————————
○———————————————————
○———————————————————
○———————————————————

To finish, turn to 'Your Key Learning Points' and write down a few sentences to summarise the key things that you have learned from this session.

influencers 15. How 2

Session 16
Putting It All Together

Session aim:

Actually, there is no Session 16! Session 16 is up to you. You're writing the next pages. Not with pen and paper but with your choices. Through the way you live your life, through the things you say and the things you do, you're affecting God's creation. The story of this world is being written day by day, moment by moment and second by second. This is where, if you haven't already, you pick up Matthew 28:18 and make it your own.

Write out Matthew 28:18 in your own words.

Get motivated!

Every influencer helps fashion this story, extending the kingdom, impacting people with the good news of God. Every breath and choice influences the future. Some choices are hard and others are easier, but all have unlimited potential. God is longing for an obedient generation, one willing to follow, serve and obey. Maybe your generation will answer His call, saying, 'Whatever the price, whatever the cost, I will follow. For we know we were born for such a time as this.'

Write a short prayer outlining a promise to God you'd like to make in the light of your reading *Influencers*.

○ _____

○ _____

○ _____

Get active!

Go and live day by day, choosing God first, loving the lost and thinking of others first. Remember, you know the secret to life now and life for eternity. Don't be precious with the secret. Shout it from the roof tops, sing it in the playgrounds and wrestle for it in the classrooms. Being an influencer is hard work. You'll take a few knocks and be asked hard questions. Don't forget your mentor. Keep them involved and up to date with your journey.

Massive blessings.

To finish, turn to 'Your Key Learning Points' and write down a few sentences to summarise the key things that you have learned from this session.

influencers 16. Putting It All Together